second edition

Copymasters

Green Level

ROSE GRIFFITHS

Heinemann Educational Publishers
Halley Court, Jordan Hill, Oxford, OX2 8EJ
a division of Harcourt Education Ltd
www.myprimary.co.uk

Heinemann is a registered trademark of Harcourt Education Ltd

First edition first published 1996

Second edition first published 2005

10 09 08 87 06 05
10 9 8 7 6 5 4 3 2 1

ISBN 0 435 02148 6

Designed and typeset by Susan Clarke
Illustrated by Mick Reid
Cover design by Susan Clarke
Repro by Digital Imaging, Glasgow
Printed and bound in the UK by Thomson Litho

The author and publishers would like to thank teachers at the
following schools for their help in trialling these materials:
Folville Junior School, Leicester
Knighton Fields Primary School, Leicester
Plymouth Grove Primary School, Manchester
Emmer Green Primary School, Reading
St John's CE (Controlled) Primary School, Sevenoaks

Contents

Part 1		
Counting pieces	Counting to 100	G1
Spell to one hundred	Spelling twenty to one hundred	G2, G3
Elevens	Addition and subtraction bonds to 11	G4
Disco	Addition of three numbers within 30	G5, G6
Ten times table	Ten times table	G7, G8
Twelves	Addition and subtraction bonds to 12	G9
Speedy sums I/Speedy sums J	Mental recall of bonds within 12	G10
Twenty to forty	Addition within 40	G11
Half each	Finding half of a group	G12, G13
Tables square	Making and using a tables square	G14, G15
Snacks	Addition and subtraction within 50	G16, G17
More adding	Addition within 50	G18, G19
Cinema	Mixed problems	G20, G21
Marbles	Multiples of 4 to 20	G22, G23
Ninety-nine game	Spelling 20 to 99	G24, G25, G26 **GP**
Elevens game	Addition and subtraction bonds to 11	G27, G28 **GP**
Twelves game	Addition and subtraction bonds to 12	G29, G30
Part 2		
Mazes	Counting to 110	G31
One hundred and more	Counting in 10s and 1s to 110	G32, G33
Thirteens	Addition and subtraction bonds to 13	G34
Darts	Addition of three numbers within 30	G35, G36
Money	Using amounts below and above £1	G37, G38
Fourteen days	Addition and subtraction bonds to 14	G39, G40
Speedy sums K/Speedy sums L	Mental recall of bonds within 14	G41
Taking away	Subtraction within 50	G42
Dice puzzles	Mixed problems	G43, G44
More taking away	Subtraction within 55	G45, G46
Jumble sale	Using money	G47, G48
Halving	Finding half of a group	G49, G50

Sums with words	Addition and subtraction within 55	G51, G52
Doubling	Mixed problems	G53, G54
Sums which make 13 game	Addition and subtraction bonds to 13	G55, G56, G57
Make 14 game	Addition and subtraction bonds to 14	G58, G59 **GP**
Jumble sale game	Using money	G60, G61 **GP**
Part 3		
Tens and ones	Counting to 120	G62
Number words	Spelling number words	G63, G64
Four times table	Four times table	G65, G66
Games	Addition and subtraction bonds to 15	G67, G68
What comes next?	Number patterns	G69, G70
Speedy sums M/Speedy sums N	Mental recall of bonds within 15	G71
Number line	Addition and subtraction within 60	G72, G73, G74
Four cards	Mixed problems	G75, G76
Twins	Halving and doubling	G77, G78
Quarter hours	Using quarters; telling the time	G79, G80
Making sixty	Addition and subtraction within 60	G81, G82
Pens in packs	Multiplication and division by 2, 3, 4 and 5	G83, G84
Day trip	Mixed problems	G85, G86
In your head	Addition and subtraction within 60	G87, G88
Fifteens game	Addition and subtraction bonds to 15	G89, G90
Double your money game	Doubling within 100	G91, G92 **GP**

GP   Colour versions of these games are included in the *Games Pack*.

Counting pieces

Name _____

Date _____

Draw the missing pieces.

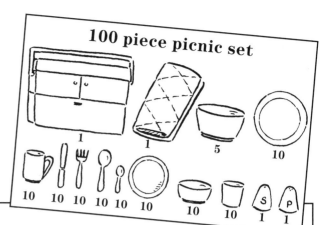

100 piece picnic set

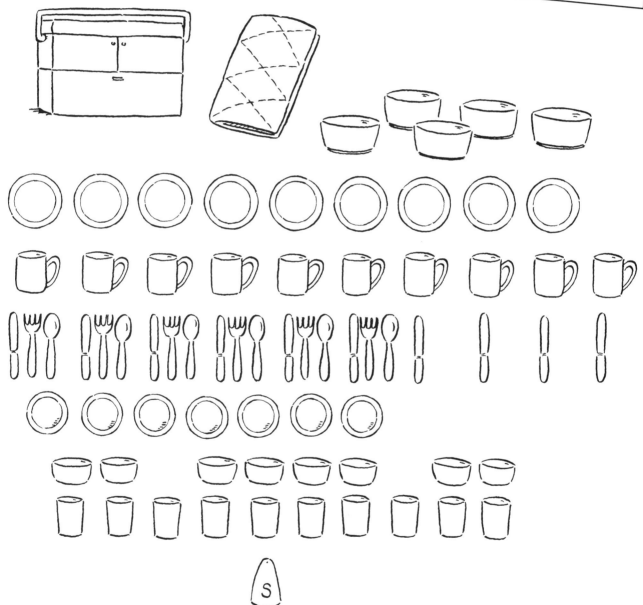

Are there 100 pieces? _____

Counting to 100   ◄ Green Pupil Book Part 1 pages 8 and 9

Spell to one hundred

Fill in the missing letters.

Name _____

Date _____

20
t w e n t y
t w _____

30
t h i r t y
t h _____

40
f o r t y
f _____

50
f i f t y
f _____

60
s i x t y
s _____

70
s e v e n t y
s _____

80
e i g h t y
e i g h ___
e i _____
e _____
_____
e i g h t y

90
n i n e t y
n i n e ___
n i _____
n _____
_____
n i n e t y

100
h u n d r e d
h u n _____
h u _____
h _____
_____
h u n d r e d

Mixed up numbers! Sort them out.

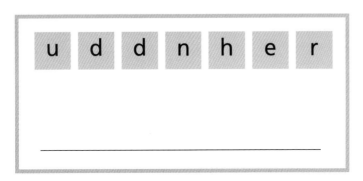

u d d n h e r

_____

t y x i s

_____

Spell to one hundred

Name _____

Date _____

Draw tens and ones.
Write the number in words.

42

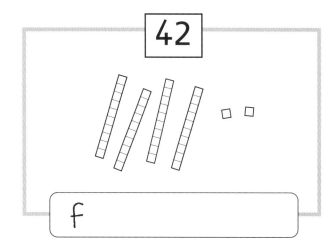

f

51

60

85

74

63

91

Number Connections © Rose Griffiths 2005
Harcourt Education Ltd

Elevens

Name _____

Date _____

Fill in the missing numbers.

5 + ☐ = 11   ☐ + 1 = 11

8 + ☐ = 11   ☐ + 5 = 11

4 + ☐ = 11   ☐ + 4 = 11

7 + ☐ = 11   ☐ + 3 = 11

2 + ☐ = 11   ☐ + 7 = 11

Check

7 + ☐ = 11   3 + ☐ = 11

☐ + 7 = 11   ☐ + 3 = 11

11 − 1 = ___	11 − 2 = ___	11 − 10 = ___
11 − 5 = ___	11 − 7 = ___	11 − 3 = ___
11 − 9 = ___	11 − 0 = ___	11 − 5 = ___
11 − 6 = ___	11 − 3 = ___	11 − 7 = ___
11 − 11 = ___	11 − 8 = ___	11 − 4 = ___

Disco

Name _____

Date _____

Add up these scores.

| 2 | 6 | 5 | ____ | | 4 | 5 | 7 | ____ |

| 5 | 6 | 6 | ____ | | 9 | 8 | 10 | ____ |

| 3 | 3 | 4 | ____ | | 7 | 7 | 5 | ____ |

| 6 | 8 | 6 | ____ | | 6 | 3 | 4 | ____ |

Talk to a friend about <u>how</u> you added up the scores.

G5

Disco

Name _____

Date _____

Fill in the missing scores.

I scored 6.
| 2 | 2 | |

I scored 15.
| 5 | | 5 |

I scored 30.
| | 10 | 10 |

I scored 21.
| 7 | 7 | |

I scored 12.
| 4 | | 4 |

I scored 24.
| 8 | | 8 |

I scored 27.
| 9 | 9 | |

I scored 9.
| | 3 | 3 |

I scored 18.
| 6 | | 6 |

What is special about all these scores?

_____

_____

Ten times table

Name _____

Date _____

Cut out the eleven tables facts.
Fold along the dotted line and glue flat.

Ask your teacher how to practise with these.

		5×10	50
0×10	0	6×10	60
1×10	10	7×10	70
2×10	20	8×10	80
3×10	30	9×10	90
4×10	40	10×10	100

Ten times table

Name _____

Date _____

Fill in the missing numbers.   Check.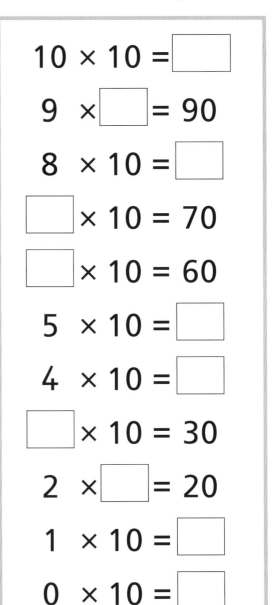

8 × 10 = ☐
10 × 8 = ☐

5 × 10 = ☐
10 × 5 = ☐

10 × 1 = ☐
1 × 10 = ☐

7 × 10 = ☐
10 × 7 = ☐

10 × 10 = ☐
9 × ☐ = 90
8 × 10 = ☐
☐ × 10 = 70
☐ × 10 = 60
5 × 10 = ☐
4 × 10 = ☐
☐ × 10 = 30
2 × ☐ = 20
1 × 10 = ☐
0 × 10 = ☐

What is 9 times 10?

_____

What is 10 times 9?

_____

Twelves

Name _____

Date _____

Fill in the missing numbers.

☐ + 2 = 12

☐ + 11 = 12

☐ + 3 = 12

☐ + 1 = 12

☐ + 8 = 12

4 + ☐ = 12

7 + ☐ = 12

6 + ☐ = 12

5 + ☐ = 12

10 + ☐ = 12

Check

5 + ☐ = 12

☐ + 5 = 12

9 + ☐ = 12

☐ + 9 = 12

12 – 2 = ___

12 – 6 = ___

12 – 0 = ___

12 – 3 = ___

12 – 7 = ___

12 – 1 = ___

12 – 12 = ___

12 – 8 = ___

12 – 4 = ___

12 – 11 = ___

12 – 4 = ___

12 – 5 = ___

12 – 7 = ___

12 – 10 = ___

12 – 9 = ___

Addition and subtraction bonds to 12 ◄ Green Pupil Book Part 1 pages 18 and 19   *Number Connections* © Rose Griffiths 2005
Harcourt Education Ltd

Speedy sums I

1 2 3 minute test

Name _____

Date _____

4 + 5 = ____   8 – 5 = ____   10 + 2 = ____

7 + 2 = ____   11 – 7 = ____   10 – 8 = ____

9 + 3 = ____   5 – 3 = ____   6 + 5 = ____

1 + 11 = ____   12 – 7 = ____   11 – 4 = ____

6 + 4 = ____   9 – 1 = ____   3 + 5 = ____

0 + 9 = ____   11 – 2 = ____   10 – 3 = ____

3 + 6 = ____   11 – 3 = ____    Score: ____

Mental recall of bonds within 12 ◀ Green Pupil Book Part 1 pages 20 and 21 onwards

Number Connections © Rose Griffiths 2005 Harcourt Education Ltd

✂ -

Speedy sums J

1 2 3 minute test

Name _____

Date _____

8 + 4 = ____   12 – 10 = ____   10 + 1 = ____

6 + 3 = ____   10 – 2 = ____   12 – 4 = ____

2 + 7 = ____   12 – 6 = ____   4 + 4 = ____

5 + 5 = ____   6 – 4 = ____   8 – 6 = ____

3 + 9 = ____   10 – 6 = ____   5 + 4 = ____

6 + 0 = ____   11 – 5 = ____   10 – 7 = ____

8 + 3 = ____   12 – 7 = ____   Score: ____

Mental recall of bonds within 12 ◀ Green Pupil Book Part 1 pages 20 and 21 onwards

Number Connections © Rose Griffiths 2005 Harcourt Education Ltd

Twenty to forty

Name _____

Date _____

G11

Use tens and ones.

```
 24 ◄ [▭▭▭▭▭▭▭▭ ▫▫▫▫]
+ 12 ◄ [▭▭▭▭▭▭ ▫▫]
____

____
```

```
 18 ◄ [▭▭▭▭▭▭ ▫▫▫▫▫ ▫▫▫]
+ 17 ◄ [▭▭▭▭▭▭▭ ▫▫▫▫▫ ▫▫]
____

____
```

Draw tens and ones.

```
 15 ◄ [        ]
+ 23 ◄ [        ]
____

____
```

```
 19 ◄ [        ]
+ 17 ◄ [        ]
____

____
```

```
 22 ◄ [        ]
+ 19 ◄ [        ]
____

____
```

```
 20 ◄ [        ]
+ 10 ◄ [        ]
____

____
```

```
 14 ◄ [        ]
+ 17 ◄ [        ]
____

____
```

```
 16 ◄ [        ]
+ 19 ◄ [        ]
____

____
```

Half each

Name _____

Date _____

You can always share an <u>even number</u> by 2.

Half each!

Use coins if you want to.

Half of 12p is _____

Half of 20p is _____

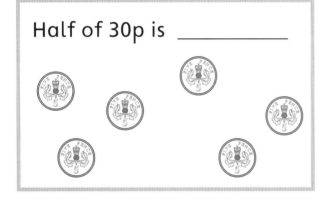

Half of 30p is _____

Half of 44p is _____

Half of 10p is _____ $\boxed{1}\boxed{0} \div \boxed{2} = $ ___

Half of 20p is _____ $\boxed{2}\boxed{0} \div \boxed{2} = $ ___

Half of 30p is _____ $\boxed{3}\boxed{0} \div \boxed{2} = $ ___

Half of 40p is _____ $\boxed{4}\boxed{0} \div \boxed{2} = $ ___

Half of 50p is _____ $\boxed{5}\boxed{0} \div \boxed{2} = $ ___

Half each

Name _____

Date _____

Use tens and ones.

Swap a ten for ten ones if you need to.

42

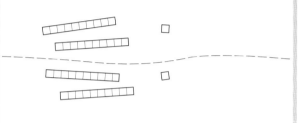

Half of 42 is _____

36

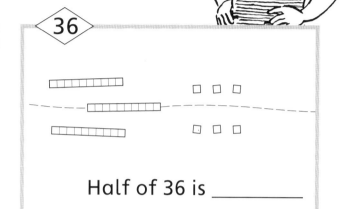

Half of 36 is _____

28

Half of 28 is _____

18

Half of 18 is _____

What is half of ...

10? _____   22? _____   34? _____

12? _____   24? _____   36? _____

14? _____   26? _____   38? _____

16? _____   28? _____   40? _____

18? _____   30? _____   42? _____

20? _____   32? _____   44? _____

Tables square

Name _____

Date _____

Fill in the missing numbers.

0 × 0 =	0 × 1 =	0 × 3 =	0 × 4 =
1 × 0 =	1 × 1 =	1 × 3 =	1 × 4 =
2 × 0 =	2 × 1 =	2 × 3 =	2 × 4 =
3 × 0 =	3 × 1 =	3 × 3 =	3 × 4 =
4 × 0 =	4 × 1 =	4 × 3 =	4 × 4 =
5 × 0 =	5 × 1 =	5 × 3 =	5 × 4 =

Finish this tables square.

Keep it in your book.

×	0	1	2	3	4	5
0						
1						
2						
3						
4						
5						

This tables square belongs to _____

Tables square

Name _____

Date _____

Fill in the missing numbers.
Check on your tables square. ✓ or ✗

$2 \times 3 =$ _____ $\qquad$ $0 \times 3 =$ _____ $\qquad$ $1 \times 3 =$ _____

$5 \times 3 =$ _____ $\qquad$ $4 \times 3 =$ _____ $\qquad$ $3 \times 3 =$ _____

$3 \times 2 =$ _____ $\qquad$ $5 \times 2 =$ _____ $\qquad$ $2 \times 2 =$ _____

$1 \times 2 =$ _____ $\qquad$ $0 \times 2 =$ _____ $\qquad$ $4 \times 2 =$ _____

$0 \times 4 =$ _____ $\qquad$ $3 \times 4 =$ _____ $\qquad$ $5 \times 4 =$ _____

$4 \times 4 =$ _____ $\qquad$ $2 \times 4 =$ _____ $\qquad$ $1 \times 4 =$ _____

$\square \times 5 = 10$	$\square \times 3 = 3$	$\square \times 4 = 12$
$\square \times 5 = 25$	$\square \times 3 = 12$	$\square \times 4 = 4$
$\square \times 5 = 20$	$\square \times 3 = 15$	$\square \times 4 = 16$
$\square \times 5 = 15$	$\square \times 3 = 6$	$\square \times 4 = 8$
$\square \times 5 = 5$	$\square \times 3 = 9$	$\square \times 4 = 20$

Making and using a tables square   ◄ Green Pupil Book Part 1 pages 28 and 29

Number Connections © Rose Griffiths 2005
Harcourt Education Ltd

Snacks

Name _____

Date _____

Use tens and ones.

34p
− 12p
_____

_____

34
− 12
_____

_____

Cross out tens and ones.

47p
− 22p
_____

_____

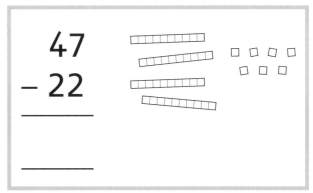

47
− 22
_____

_____

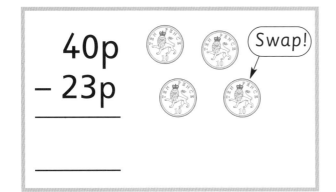

40p
− 23p
_____

_____

Swap!

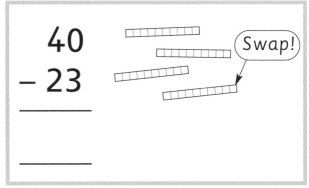

40
− 23
_____

_____

Swap!

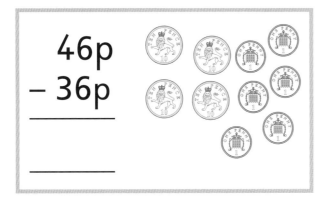

46p
− 36p
_____

_____

46
− 36
_____

_____

Snacks

Name _____

Date _____

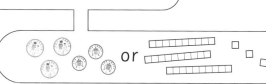

Use tens and ones ...

or

Swap a ten for ten ones if you need to.

47
− 16
_____

_____

50
− 38
_____

_____

40
− 29
_____

_____

45
− 15
_____

_____

38
− 24
_____

_____

42
− 22
_____

_____

17
− 10
_____

_____

31
− 18
_____

_____

 ✓ or ✗

49
− 27
_____

_____

26
− 17
_____

_____

50
− 30
_____

_____

37
− 23
_____

_____

18
− 18
_____

_____

46
− 27
_____

_____

39
− 35
_____

_____

30
− 16
_____

_____

Addition and subtraction within 50   ◄ Green Pupil Book Part 1 pages 28 and 29   *Number Connections* © Rose Griffiths 2005
Harcourt Education Ltd

More adding

Name _____

Date _____

Use tens and ones. Then add up on paper.

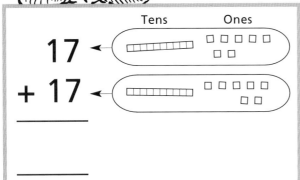

17
+ 17
_____

_____

13
+ 27
_____

_____

Draw tens and ones. Then add up on paper.

Tens   Ones

18
+ 18
_____

_____

Tens   Ones

24
+ 19
_____

_____

15
+ 24
_____

_____

36
+ 11
_____

_____

27
+ 17
_____

_____

8
+ 34
_____

_____

More adding

Name _____

Date _____

Use tens and ones. Draw them.
Then add up on paper.

	Tens	Ones
19 ←		
+ 18 ←		
_____		
_____		

	Tens	Ones
26 ←		
+ 20 ←		
_____		
_____		

```
  23        14        30        32
+ 18      + 29      + 15      +  8
————      ————      ————      ————


————      ————      ————      ————


  16        28        33        22
+ 24      + 15      + 11      + 22
————      ————      ————      ————


————      ————      ————      ————


  34        27        19
+ 15      + 18      + 19
————      ————      ————
```

Check

```
————      ————      ————
```

Cinema

Name _____

Date _____

Make up your own cinema programme.

✂

Fill in the spaces.

_____'s Cinema

Screen One	Screen Two	Screen Three
Times: 1.30 4.00 6.00	Times:	Times:

Tickets: £ _____ (adult)   £ _____ (child)

Cut out. Use with Copymaster G21. Ask your teacher how to play.

Your name

Names of films

Pictures

Times

Prices of tickets

Cinema

Use with Copymaster G20. Ask your teacher how to play.

⋆_____'s Cinema ⋆

Film: _____

Screen: _____   £ _____

⋆_____'s Cinema ⋆

Film: _____

Screen: _____   £ _____

⋆_____'s Cinema ⋆

Film: _____

Screen: _____   £ _____

⋆_____'s Cinema ⋆

Film: _____

Screen: _____   £ _____

⋆_____'s Cinema ⋆

Film: _____

Screen: _____   £ _____

⋆_____'s Cinema ⋆

Film: _____

Screen: _____   £ _____

⋆_____'s Cinema ⋆

Film: _____

Screen: _____   £ _____

⋆_____'s Cinema ⋆

Film: _____

Screen: _____   £ _____

⋆_____'s Cinema ⋆

Film: _____

Screen: _____   £ _____

⋆_____'s Cinema ⋆

Film: _____

Screen: _____   £ _____

Marbles

Name _____

Date _____

Fill in the missing numbers.

1 2 3   5 6 7   9 10 11   13 14 15   17 18 19

1	2	3	
5	6	7	
9	10	11	
13	14	15	
17	18	19	

1	2	3		5	6	7		9	10
11		13	14	15		17	18	19	

	19	18	17		15	14	13		11
10	9		7	6	5		3	2	1

0 + 4 = _____

4 + 4 = _____

8 + 4 = _____

12 + 4 = _____

16 + 4 = _____

4, _____ , 12, 16, 20

4, 8, _____ , 16, _____

20 − 4 = _____

16 − 4 = _____

8 − 4 = _____

12 − 4 = _____

4 − 4 = _____

16 − 4 = _____

Marbles

Name _____

Date _____

Score 4 points for each marble.

Draw the missing marbles.

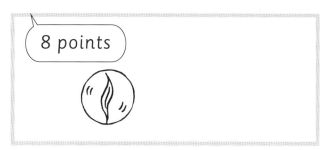

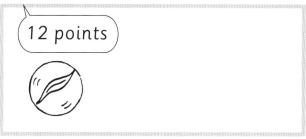

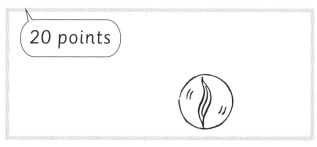

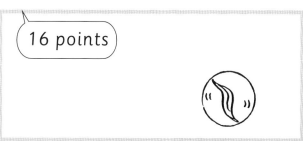

$4 + 4 =$ ___ $2 \times 4 =$ ___

$4 + 4 + 4 =$ ___ $3 \times 4 =$ ___

$4 + 4 + 4 + 4 =$ ___ $4 \times 4 =$ ___

$4 + 4 + 4 + 4 + 4 =$ ___ $5 \times 4 =$ ___

$3 \times 4 =$ ____

$4 \times 3 =$ ____

$12 \div 4 =$ ____

$12 \div 3 =$ ____

$5 \times 4 =$ ____

$4 \times 5 =$ ____

$20 \div 4 =$ ____

$20 \div 5 =$ ____

Multiples of 4 to 20   ◀ Green Pupil Book Part 1 pages 34 and 35

Number Connections © Rose Griffiths 2005
Harcourt Education Ltd

Ninety-nine game

sheet 1 of 3

Print on card if possible. Reusable.
Cut out the instructions card, 81 number cards, and 3 sets of 17 word cards.
Store in a clear zip-top wallet or in a small sandwich box.

≈ Ninety-nine ≈

A game for 1, 2 or 3 people.

- **Before you start**
  You need a set of 17 word cards each.
  Put the number cards in a tub or dish.

- **How to play**

Take a number card.
Make the number with word cards.

Ask your friend to check it.
If it is right, keep the number card.
If not, put the number card back
in the tub. You can use the word
cards again and again.

Now it is your
friend's go.

- If someone picks **99** then stop!

  Count how many number cards you won.

◄ Green Pupil Book Part 1; **Spelling twenty to ninety nine**

Number Connections © Rose Griffiths 1997
Heinemann Educational Publishers, Oxford

Ninety-nine game

G25

Print on card if possible. Reusable. Cut into 81 number cards.

GP

91	82	73	64	55	46	37	28	99
92	83	74	65	56	47	38	29	20
93	84	75	66	57	48	39	30	21
94	85	76	67	58	49	40	31	22
95	86	77	68	59	50	41	32	23
96	87	78	69	60	51	42	33	24
97	88	79	70	61	52	43	34	25
98	89	80	71	62	53	44	35	26
99	90	81	72	63	54	45	36	27

Number Connections © Rose Griffiths 2005
Harcourt Education Ltd

Ninety-nine game

sheet 3 of 3

Print on card if possible. Reusable.
Print <u>3 copies</u> to enable 3 children to play. Use 3 different colours of card, to make it easier to sort out each set of cards.
Cut into 17 word cards, with one corner cut off each.

	one
twenty	two
thirty	three
forty	four
fifty	five
sixty	six
seventy	seven
eighty	eight
ninety	nine

Ninety-nine (on each card corner)

◀ Green Pupil Book Part 1; use from pages 10 and 11 onwards

Number Connections © Rose Griffiths 2005
Harcourt Education Ltd

Elevens game

sheet 1 of 2

Print on card if possible. Reusable.
Cut out the instructions card and 18 number cards.
Store in a clear zip-top wallet or in an envelope.

≈ Elevens ≈

A game for 1, 2 or 3 people.

- **Before you start**
  Shuffle the number cards.
  Spread them out on the table, face down.

- **How to play**

Turn over 2 cards.
Add up the numbers.

If you get exactly 11,
<u>keep</u> the cards.
If not, turn the cards
back over.

Now it is your
friend's go.

- **Keep going until all the cards have gone.**

◄ Green Pupil Book Part 1; **Addition and subtraction bonds to 11**

Number Connections © Rose Griffiths 2005
Harcourt Education Ltd

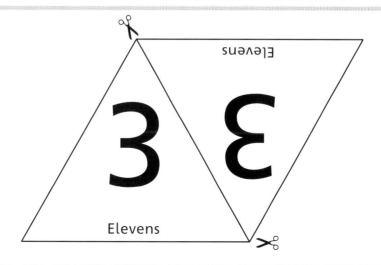

Elevens game

sheet 2 of 2

Print on card if possible. Reusable.

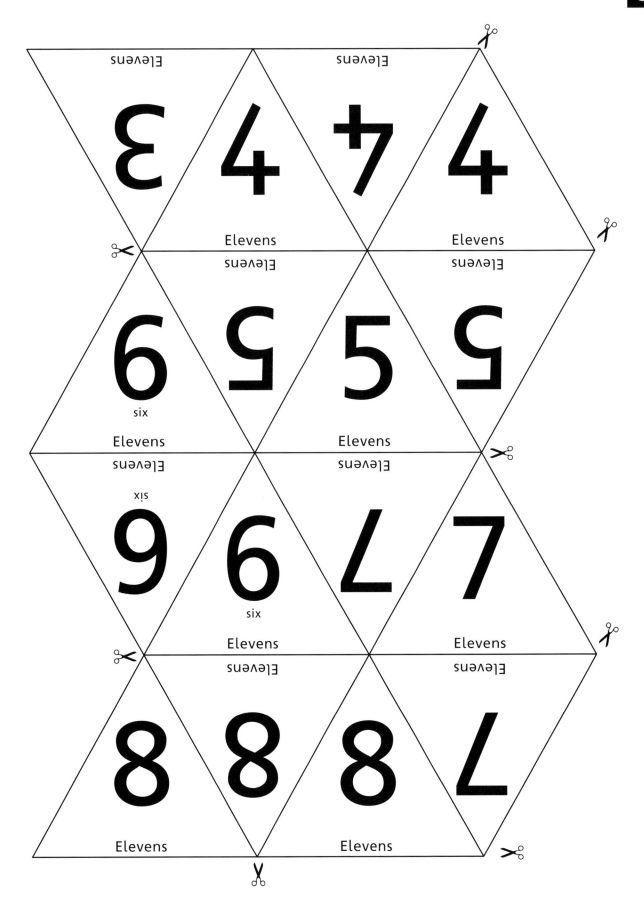

Twelves game

sheet 1 of 2

Print on card if possible. Reusable.
Cut out the instructions card and 20 number cards. Store in a clear zip-top wallet or in an envelope.

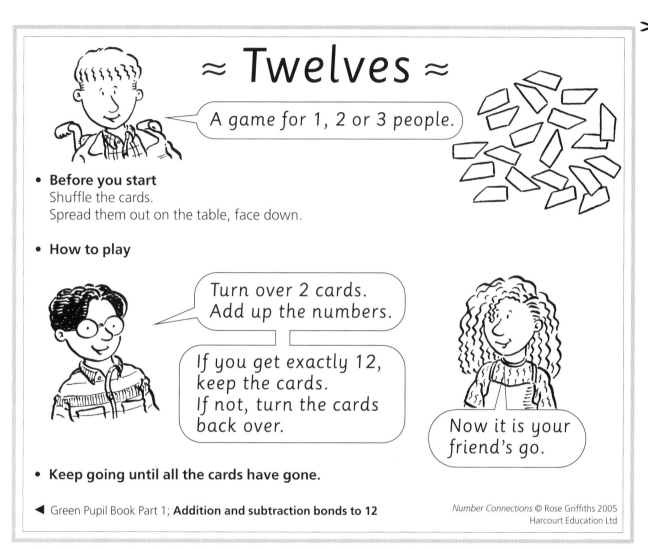

≈ Twelves ≈

A game for 1, 2 or 3 people.

- **Before you start**
  Shuffle the cards.
  Spread them out on the table, face down.

- **How to play**

Turn over 2 cards.
Add up the numbers.

If you get exactly 12,
keep the cards.
If not, turn the cards
back over.

Now it is your friend's go.

- **Keep going until all the cards have gone.**

◀ Green Pupil Book Part 1; **Addition and subtraction bonds to 12**

Number Connections © Rose Griffiths 2005
Harcourt Education Ltd

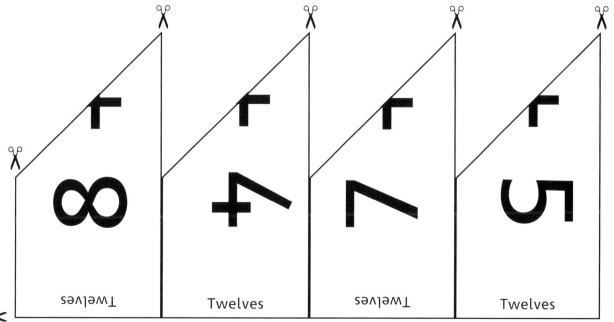

Number Connections © Rose Griffiths 2005
Harcourt Education Ltd

Twelves game

sheet 2 of 2

Print on card if possible. Reusable.

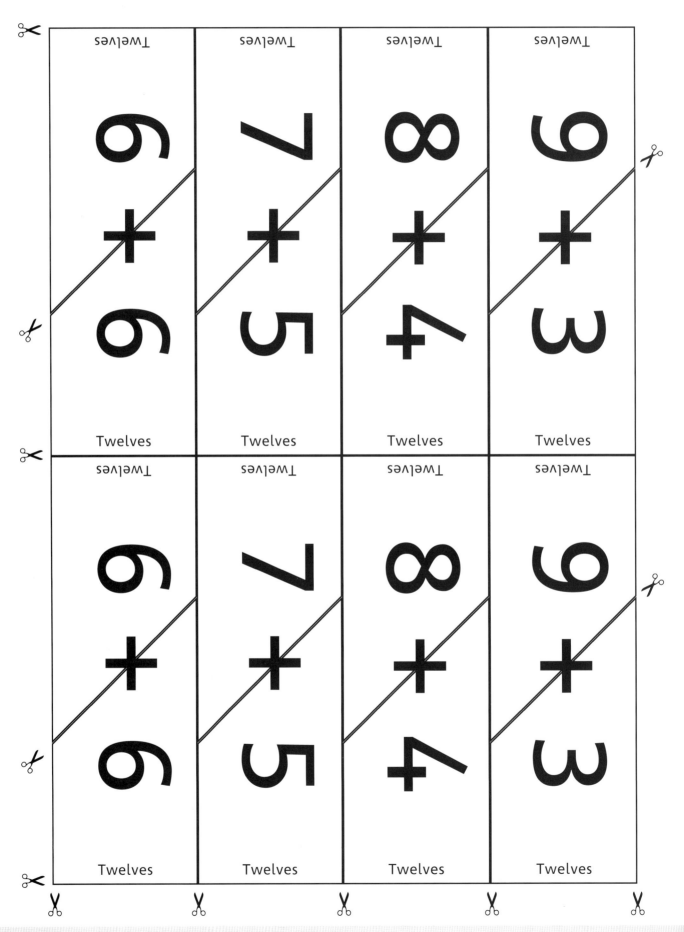

Number Connections © Rose Griffiths 2001
Harcourt Education Ltd

Mazes

Name _____

Date _____

Colour the squares.
Draw and colour more squares, to make a maze.

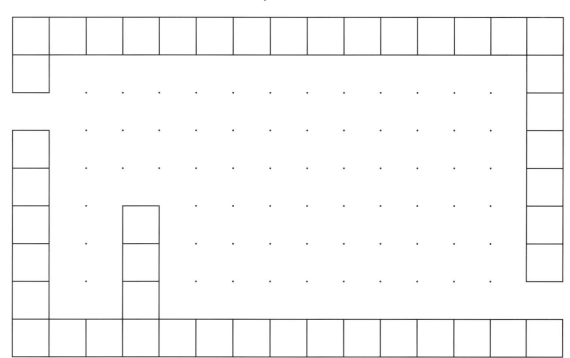

How many squares altogether? _____

Colour the squares.
Draw and colour more squares, to make a maze.

How many squares altogether? _____

Number Connections © Rose Griffiths 2005
Harcourt Education Ltd

One hundred and more

Name _____

Date _____

Write the missing numbers.

96, 97, 98, _____, _____, _____ .

103, 102, 101, _____, _____, _____ .

10, 20, 30, _____, _____, _____, 70, 80, 90, _____, _____ .

14 + 1 = _____   14 + 10 = _____

25 + 1 = _____   25 + 10 = _____

32 + 1 = _____   32 + 10 = _____

47 + 1 = _____   47 + 10 = _____

50 + 1 = _____   50 + 10 = _____

61 + 1 = _____   61 + 10 = _____

73 + 1 = _____   73 + 10 = _____

86 + 1 = _____   86 + 10 = _____

99 + 1 = _____   99 + 10 = _____

Check ✓ or ✗

100	100	100	100	100
+ 1	+ 3	+ 4	+ 7	+ 10
_____	_____	_____	_____	_____
_____	_____	_____	_____	_____

One hundred and more

Name _____

Date _____

G33

Spell these numbers.

1 _____

2 _____

3 _____

4 _____

5 _____

6 _____

7 _____

8 _____

9 _____

10 _____

11 _____

12 _____

13 _____

14 _____

15 _____

30 _____

40 _____

50 _____

60 _____

70 _____

16 _____

17 _____

18 _____

19 _____

20 _____

80 _____

90 _____

100 _____

110 _____

_____

Ask an adult to ✓ or ✗.
How many did you get right? _____

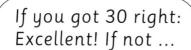

If you got 30 right:
Excellent! If not ...

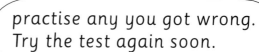

practise any you got wrong.
Try the test again soon.

Counting in 10s and 1s to 110 ◀ Green Pupil Book Part 2 pages 40 and 41

Harcourt Education Ltd

Thirteens

Name _____

Date _____

Fill in the missing numbers.

3 + ☐ = 13

5 + ☐ = 13

6 + ☐ = 13

4 + ☐ = 13

2 + ☐ = 13

☐ + 6 = 13

☐ + 7 = 13

☐ + 4 = 13

☐ + 8 = 13

☐ + 5 = 13

Check

6 + ☐ = 13

☐ + 6 = 13

4 + ☐ = 13

☐ + 4 = 13

13 − 2 = ___

13 − 8 = ___

13 −12 = ___

13 − 3 = ___

13 − 7 = ___

13 − 6 = ___

13 − 4 = ___

13 − 9 = ___

13 − 1 = ___

13 −13 = ___

13 − 0 = ___

13 − 5 = ___

13 −11 = ___

13 − 8 = ___

13 −10 = ___

Darts

Name _____

Date _____

Make up questions for a friend to do.

Draw 3 darts on each dartboard.

✂ -

These questions are for _____ .

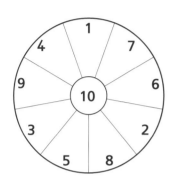

Total score: _____

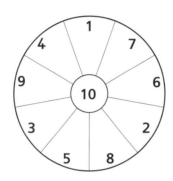

Total score: _____

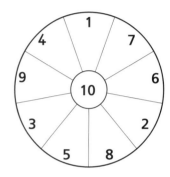

Total score: _____

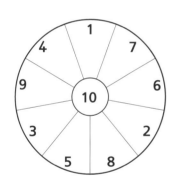

Total score: _____

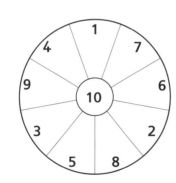

Total score: _____

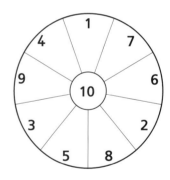

Total score: _____

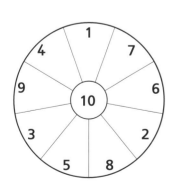

Total score: _____

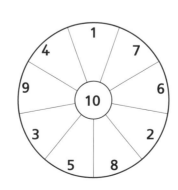

Total score: _____

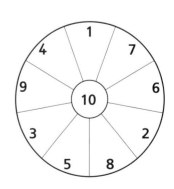

Total score: _____

Darts

Name _____

Date _____

Draw each missing dart.

Total score: 15

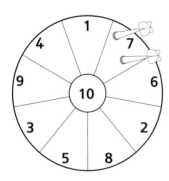

Total score: 24

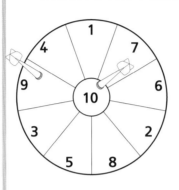

Total score: 29

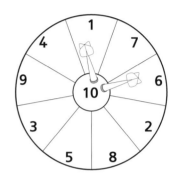

Total score: 6

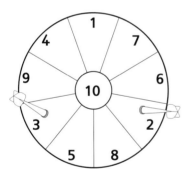

Total score: 20

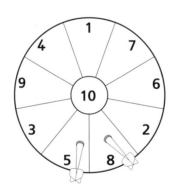

Total score: 14

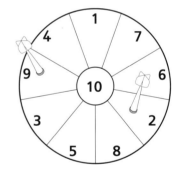

Total score: 21

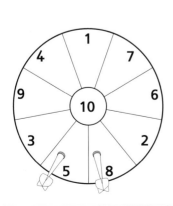

Total score: 17

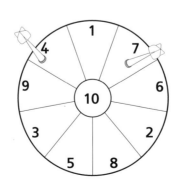

Total score: 20

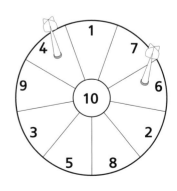

Addition of three numbers within 30 ◀ Green Pupil Book Part 2 pages 44 and 45

Number Connections © Rose Griffiths 2005
Harcourt Education Ltd

G36

Money

Name _____

Date _____

Cut out the amounts of money at the bottom.
Stick them in the right spaces.

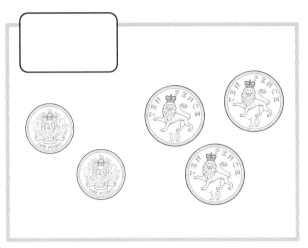
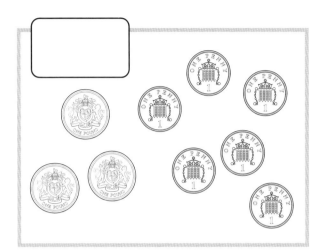
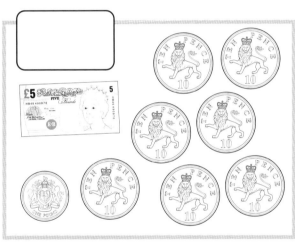
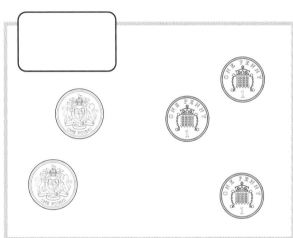

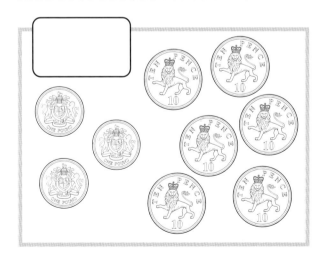

------------------------------------✂------------------------------------

| £3·06 | £3·60 | £2·03 | £2·30 | £6·07 | £6·70 |

Using amounts below and above £1   ◀ Green Pupil Book Part 2 pages 46 and 47
► Copymaster G38

Number Connections © Rose Griffiths 2005
Harcourt Education Ltd

Money

Name _____

Date _____

G38

Make each amount with coins.
Add up and write the total.

Work with a friend if you want to.

£3·50 + 27p = ☐

99p + £1·56 = ☐

£1·44 + £1·62 = ☐

£2·75 + £1·30 = ☐

50p + £2·50 = ☐

£1·90 + £1·53 = ☐

Fourteen days

Name _____

Date _____

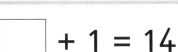

Fill in the missing numbers.

☐ + 1 = 14

☐ + 6 = 14

☐ + 9 = 14

☐ + 2 = 14

☐ + 7 = 14

3 + ☐ = 14

8 + ☐ = 14

11 + ☐ = 14

5 + ☐ = 14

10 + ☐ = 14

Check

8 + ☐ = 14

☐ + 8 = 14

5 + ☐ = 14

☐ + 5 = 14

14 − 0 = ____

14 − 7 = ____

14 − 10 = ____

14 − 4 = ____

14 − 13 = ____

14 − 6 = ____

14 − 1 = ____

14 − 3 = ____

14 − 8 = ____

14 − 11 = ____

14 − 2 = ____

14 − 5 = ____

14 − 12 = ____

14 − 14 = ____

14 − 9 = ____

Number Connections © Rose Griffiths 2005
Harcourt Education Ltd

Fourteen days

Name _____

Date _____

Fill in the missing letters.

Mon.

Monday
Mon_____
M_____
_____

Sun.

Sunday
Sun_____
S_____
_____

Tues.

Tuesday
Tues_____
T_____
_____

Wed.

Wednesday
Wednes_____
Wed_____
W_____
_____

Sat.

Saturday
Satur_____
Sat_____
S_____
_____

Thurs.

Thursday
Thurs_____
_____

Fri.

Friday
Fri_____
_____

14 days

fortnight
fort_____
_____

Speedy sums Ⓚ

1 2 3 minute test

Name _____

Date _____

6 + 3 + 4 = _____   8 + 5 = _____   14 − 5 = _____

2 + 1 + 7 = _____   3 + 4 = _____   12 − 8 = _____

1 + 5 + 8 = _____   5 + 8 = _____   7 − 2 = _____

3 + 3 + 4 = _____   11 + 3 = _____   14 − 7 = _____

4 + 3 + 5 = _____   10 + 3 = _____   10 − 5 = _____

0 + 7 + 7 = _____   8 + 3 = _____   13 − 9 = _____

8 + 1 + 2 = _____   4 + 5 = _____   Score: _____

Mental recall of bonds within 14 onwards ◀ Green Pupil Book Part 2 pages 50 and 51   *Number Connections* © Rose Griffiths 2005 Harcourt Education Ltd

Speedy sums Ⓛ

1 2 3 minute test

Name _____

Date _____

5 + 2 + 3 = _____   6 + 7 = _____   14 − 10 = _____

1 + 6 + 6 = _____   11 + 2 = _____   12 − 6 = _____

4 + 0 + 10 = _____   5 + 9 = _____   9 − 3 = _____

3 + 1 + 8 = _____   4 + 6 = _____   12 − 7 = _____

6 + 6 + 2 = _____   3 + 10 = _____   11 − 3 = _____

7 + 3 + 2 = _____   9 + 3 = _____   11 − 5 = _____

2 + 3 + 6 = _____   7 + 4 = _____   Score: _____

Mental recall of bonds within 14 onwards ◀ Green Pupil Book Part 2 pages 50 and 51   *Number Connections* © Rose Griffiths 2005 Harcourt Education Ltd

Taking away

Name _____

Date _____

Use tens and ones.

50	40	30	20
− 9	− 9	− 9	− 9
———	———	———	———
———	———	———	———

50	40	30	20
− 6	− 6	− 6	− 6
———	———	———	———
———	———	———	———

Cross out tens and ones.

Swap a ten for ten ones if you need to.

47
− 23
———

———

50
− 24
———

Swap!

———

42
− 28
———

———

35
− 14
———

———

Dice puzzles

Name _____

Date _____

Add up the totals.

$1+1+1+1 =$ _____ $4 \times 1 =$ _____

$2+2+2+2 =$ _____ $4 \times 2 =$ _____

$3+3+3+3 =$ _____ $4 \times 3 =$ _____

$4+4+4+4 =$ _____ $4 \times 4 =$ _____

$5+5+5+5 =$ _____ $4 \times 5 =$ _____

$6+6+6+6 =$ _____ $4 \times 6 =$ _____

$3 \times 1 =$ _____ $2 \times 1 =$ _____

$3 \times 2 =$ _____ $2 \times 2 =$ _____

$3 \times 3 =$ _____ $2 \times 3 =$ _____

$3 \times 4 =$ _____ $2 \times 4 =$ _____

$3 \times 5 =$ _____ $2 \times 5 =$ _____

$3 \times 6 =$ _____ $2 \times 6 =$ _____

Mixed problems   ◄ Green Pupil Book Part 2 pages 54 and 55
► Copymaster G44

Number Connections © Rose Griffiths 2005
Harcourt Education Ltd

Dice puzzles

Name _____

Date _____

Draw the dots on the fourth dice.

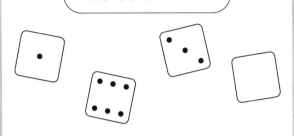

The total is 18.

The total is 24.

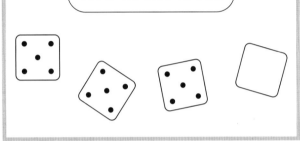

The total is 20.

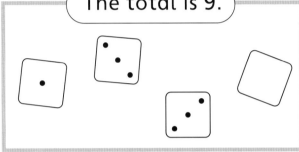

The total is 9.

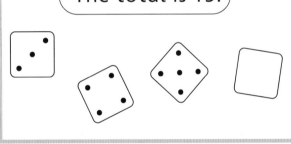

The total is 15.

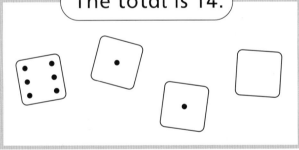

The total is 14.

Make up 2 puzzles yourself.

Ask a friend to do them.

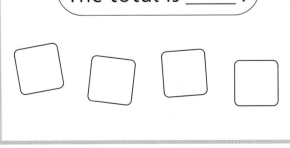

The total is _____.

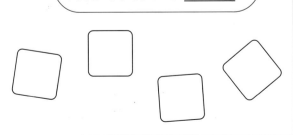

The total is _____.

More taking away

Name _____

Date _____

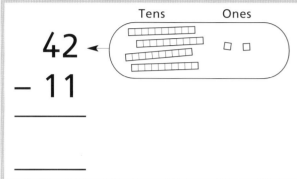

Use tens and ones.
Then take away on paper.

$\begin{array}{r} 42 \\ -\ 11 \\ \hline \\ \hline \end{array}$
Tens   Ones

$\begin{array}{r} 32 \\ -\ 17 \\ \hline \\ \hline \end{array}$
Tens   Ones

$\begin{array}{r} 41 \\ -\ 25 \\ \hline \\ \hline \end{array}$
Tens   Ones

$\begin{array}{r} 39 \\ -\ 25 \\ \hline \\ \hline \end{array}$
Tens   Ones

$\begin{array}{r} 36 \\ -\ 18 \\ \hline \\ \hline \end{array}$
$\begin{array}{r} 55 \\ -\ 36 \\ \hline \\ \hline \end{array}$
$\begin{array}{r} 43 \\ -\ 25 \\ \hline \\ \hline \end{array}$
$\begin{array}{r} 19 \\ -\ 18 \\ \hline \\ \hline \end{array}$

$\begin{array}{r} 40 \\ -\ 17 \\ \hline \\ \hline \end{array}$
$\begin{array}{r} 27 \\ -\ 27 \\ \hline \\ \hline \end{array}$
$\begin{array}{r} 52 \\ -\ 46 \\ \hline \\ \hline \end{array}$
$\begin{array}{r} 45 \\ -\ 24 \\ \hline \\ \hline \end{array}$

Subtraction within 55   ◄ Green Pupil Book Part 2 pages 56 and 57
► Copymaster G46

Number Connections © Rose Griffiths 2005
Harcourt Education Ltd

G45

More taking away

Name _____

Date _____

Use tens and ones.
Then take away on paper.

Tens	Ones

$$\begin{array}{r} 46 \\ -\ 23 \\ \hline \\ \hline \end{array}$$

Tens	Ones

$$\begin{array}{r} 32 \\ -\ 18 \\ \hline \\ \hline \end{array}$$

$$\begin{array}{r} 44 \\ -\ 26 \\ \hline \\ \hline \end{array}$$
$$\begin{array}{r} 28 \\ -\ 27 \\ \hline \\ \hline \end{array}$$
$$\begin{array}{r} 40 \\ -\ 23 \\ \hline \\ \hline \end{array}$$
$$\begin{array}{r} 55 \\ -\ 38 \\ \hline \\ \hline \end{array}$$

$$\begin{array}{r} 39 \\ -\ 27 \\ \hline \\ \hline \end{array}$$
$$\begin{array}{r} 41 \\ -\ 28 \\ \hline \\ \hline \end{array}$$
$$\begin{array}{r} 22 \\ -\ 9 \\ \hline \\ \hline \end{array}$$
$$\begin{array}{r} 35 \\ -\ 15 \\ \hline \\ \hline \end{array}$$

$$\begin{array}{r} 52 \\ -\ 36 \\ \hline \\ \hline \end{array}$$
$$\begin{array}{r} 34 \\ -\ 34 \\ \hline \\ \hline \end{array}$$
$$\begin{array}{r} 42 \\ -\ 17 \\ \hline \\ \hline \end{array}$$

 ✓ or ✗

Number Connections © Rose Griffiths 200
Harcourt Education L

Jumble sale

Name _____

Date _____

Biscuits
3p each

Squash
5p a cup

Fill in these charts.

How many biscuits?	Total cost	How many cups of squash?	Total cost
0	0	0	
1	3p	1	
2		2	
3		3	
4		4	
5		5	
6		6	
7		7	
8		8	
9		9	
10		10	

How much for 3 biscuits and 2 cups of squash? _____

How much for 5 cups of squash and 5 biscuits? _____

Number Connections © Rose Griffiths 2005
Harcourt Education Ltd

Jumble sale

Name _____

Date _____

Use the charts on Copymaster G47.

How much for 3 biscuits and 3 cups of squash? _____

How much for 1 biscuit and 2 cups of squash? _____

How much for 6 biscuits and 3 cups of squash? _____

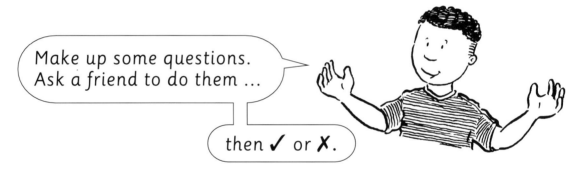

Make up some questions. Ask a friend to do them ...

then ✔ or ✗.

How much for ____ biscuits and ____ cups of squash? _____

How much for ____ biscuits and ____ cups of squash? _____

How much for ____ biscuits and ____ cups of squash? _____

How much for ____ biscuits and ____ cups of squash? _____

How much for ____ biscuits and ____ cups of squash? _____

Number Connections © Rose Griffiths 200
Harcourt Education L

Halving

Name _____

Date _____

We're sharing marbles.

You can't cut them in half, so sometimes there is one left over.

Use marbles or counters.

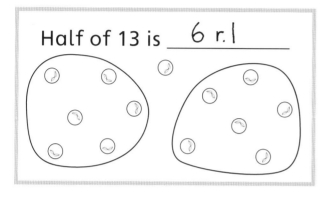

Half of 13 is ___6 r.1___

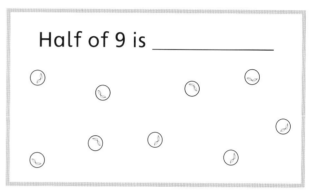

Half of 9 is _____

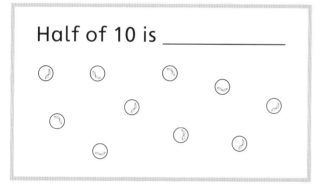

Half of 10 is _____

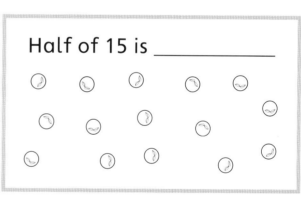

Half of 15 is _____

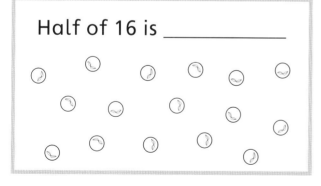

Half of 16 is _____

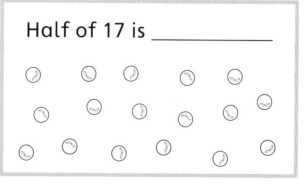

Half of 17 is _____

$16 \div 2 = $ _____ $17 \div 2 = $ _____

The calculator doesn't know we're sharing marbles!

Finding half of a group

◄ Green Pupil Book Part 2 pages 60 and 61
► Copymaster G50

Number Connections © Rose Griffiths 2005
Harcourt Education Ltd

Halving

Name _____

Date _____

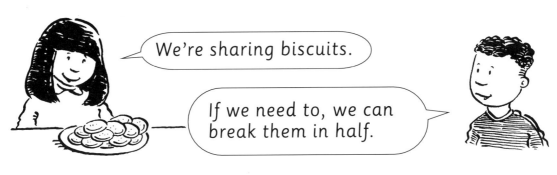

Half of 12 is _____

Half of 13 is _____

Use biscuits! (or counters) then a calculator.

Half of 14 is _____
$1\ 4 \div 2 =$ _____

Half of 20 is _____
$2\ 0 \div 2 =$ _____

Half of 21 is _____
$2\ 1 \div 2 =$ _____

Half of 33 is _____
$3\ 3 \div 2 =$ _____

Half of 34 is _____
$3\ 4 \div 2 =$ _____

Half of 46 is _____
$4\ 6 \div 2 =$ _____

Half of 47 is _____
$4\ 7 \div 2 =$ _____

Sums with words

Name _____

Date _____

Work with a friend.
Talk about these sums.

Cut them out.
Sort them into 2 piles.
Stick them in your book in 2 groups.

Sums I can do in my head.	Sums I need to write down.
Fifty-four take away two	Forty take away thirty-six
Thirty add six	Twenty-seven take away twenty-seven
Fifty-four take away twenty-three	Seventeen add seventeen
Twenty add thirty	Twenty-seven add nineteen

Sums with words

Name _____

Date _____

Write each sum and work it out.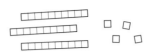

Forty-six add six

$$\begin{array}{r} 46 \\ +\ 6 \\ \hline \\ \hline \end{array}$$

Thirty-two add twenty-two

Thirty-six take away seventeen

Twenty-nine take away six

Thirty-eight add thirteen

Fifty-three take away twenty-five

Twenty-six add twenty-three

Eight add forty-two

Doubling

Name _____

Date _____

Double our money!

Draw coins to double the money in each box.

Double 24p is _____

Double 60p is _____

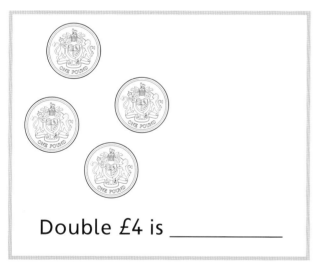

Double £4 is _____

Double 53p is _____

Double £1·20 is _____

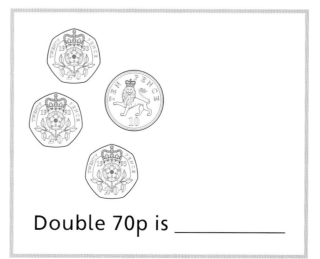

Double 70p is _____

Mixed problems   ◄ Green Pupil Book Part 2 pages 64 and 65
                     ► Copymaster G54

Number Connections © Rose Griffiths 2005

Harcourt Education Ltd

Doubling

Name _____

Date _____

Draw tens and ones to double the number in each box.

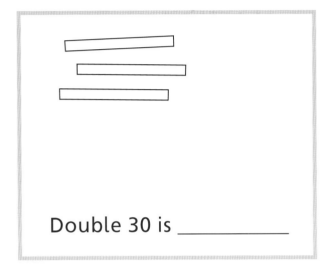

Double 30 is _____

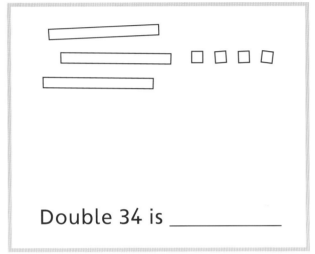

Double 34 is _____

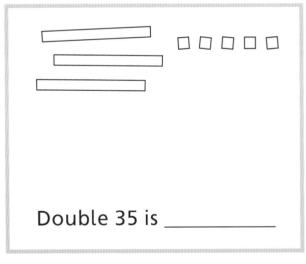

Double 35 is _____

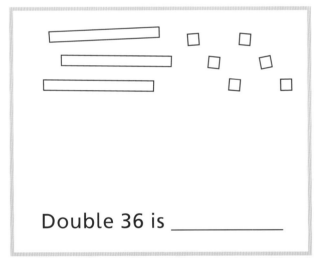

Double 36 is _____

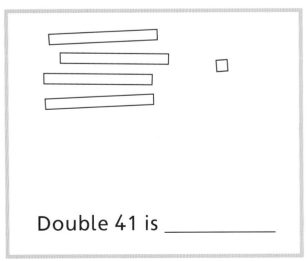

Double 41 is _____

Double 45 is _____

Print on card if possible. Reusable.
Cut out the instructions card, 3 sum cards, and 40 number cards.
Store in a clear zip-top wallet or in an envelope.

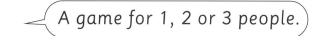

≈ Sums which make 13 ≈

A game for 1, 2 or 3 people.

- **Before you start**
  Take a sum card each.
  Shuffle the number cards.
  Put them in a pile on the table, face down.

- **How to play**
  Can you make 4 different sums which make 13?

Take the top number card.
Put it on your sum card,
or (if you don't want it)
put it at the bottom of the pile.

Now it is your
friend's go.

- **Keep going until you have all filled your cards.**
  Who finished first?

◄ Green Pupil Book Part 2; **Addition and subtraction bonds to 13**

Number Connections © Rose Griffiths 2005
Harcourt Education Ltd

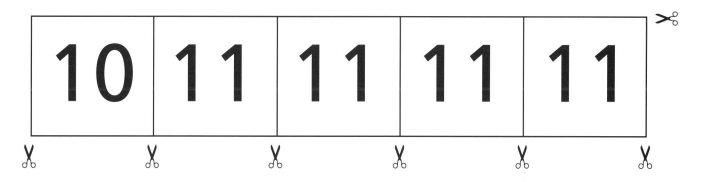

Number Connections © Rose Griffiths 2005
Harcourt Education Ltd

Sums which make 13

sheet 2 of 3

Print on card if possible. Reusable.

2	2	2	2	3
3	3	3	4	4
4	4	5	5	5
5	6 six	6 six	6 six	6 six
7	7	7	7	8
8	8	8	9 nine	9 nine
9 nine	9 nine	10	10	10

◄ Green Pupil Book Part 2; use from pages 42 and 43 onwards

Number Connections © Rose Griffiths 20C
Harcourt Education L

Print 3 copies, on card if possible. Reusable.

≈ *Sums which make 13* ≈

☐ **+** ☐ **= 13**

☐ **+** ☐ **= 13**

☐ **+** ☐ **= 13**

☐ **+** ☐ **= 13**

Make 14 game

sheet 1 of 2

Print on card if possible. Reusable.
Cut out the instructions card and 20 playing cards.
Store in a clear zip-top wallet or in an envelope.

≈ Make 14 ≈

A game for 1, 2 or 3 people.

- **Before you start**
  Shuffle the cards.
  Spread them out on the table, face down.

- **How to play**

Turn over 2 cards.
Add up the numbers.

If you get exactly 14,
<u>keep</u> the cards.
If not, turn the cards
back over.

Now it is your
friend's go.

- **Keep going until all the cards have gone.**

◀ Green Pupil Book Part 2; **Addition and subtraction bonds to 14**

Number Connections © Rose Griffiths 2005
Harcourt Education Ltd

Make 14	Make 14	Make 14	Make 14
4	4	5	5

Make 14 game

sheet 2 of 2

Print on card if possible. Reusable.

GP

Make 14 **5**	Make 14 **6** six	Make 14 **6** six	Make 14 **6** six
Make 14 **7**	Make 14 **7**	Make 14 **7**	Make 14 **7**
Make 14 **8**	Make 14 **8**	Make 14 **8**	Make 14 **9** nine
Make 14 **9** nine	Make 14 **9** nine	Make 14 **10**	Make 14 **10**

Number Connections © Rose Griffiths 2005
Harcourt Education Ltd

Jumble sale game

sheet 1 of 2

Print on card if possible. Reusable.
Colour and cut out the instructions card and 20 playing cards.
Store in a clear zip-top wallet or in an envelope.

≈ Jumble sale ≈

A game for 1, 2 or 3 people.

- **Before you start**
  Shuffle the cards.
  Spread them out on the table, face down.
  You need £1 each (a 50p, a 20p, two 10p and two 5p coins)
  and a money pot.

- **How to play**

  Turn over a card.
  Do you want to buy that item?

  If you do, put the money in the pot.
  If not, turn the card back over.

  Now it is your friend's go.

- **Keep going until you can't spend any more money.**

◀ Green Pupil Book Part 2; **Using money**

Number Connections © Rose Griffiths 2005
Harcourt Education Ltd

| Jumble sale | Jumble sale | Jumble sale | Jumble sale |
| 20p | 20p | 20p | 20p |

Jumble sale game

sheet 2 of 2

T

Print on card if possible. Reusable.

GP

Jumble sale	Jumble sale	Jumble sale	Jumble sale
75p	75p	20p	30p
Jumble sale	Jumble sale	Jumble sale	Jumble sale
30p	30p	10p	10p
Jumble sale	Jumble sale	Jumble sale	Jumble sale
10p	10p	10p	10p
Jumble sale	Jumble sale	Jumble sale	Jumble sale
5p	5p	5p	5p

◄ Green Pupil Book Part 2; use from pages 58 and 59 onwards

Number Connections © Rose Griffiths 2005
Harcourt Education Ltd

Tens and ones

Name _____

Date _____

How many in each box?

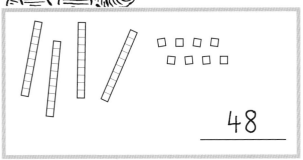
48 _____

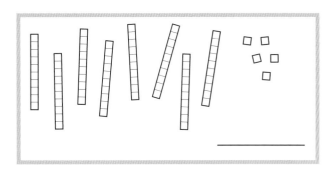
_____

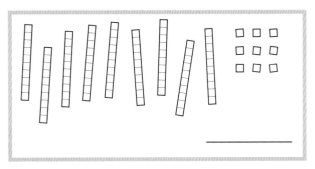
_____

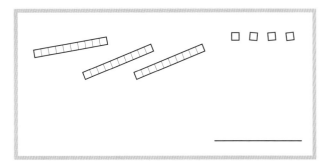
_____

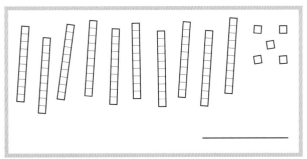
_____

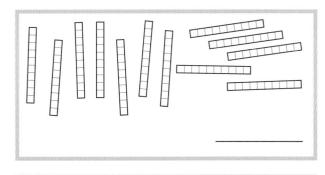
_____

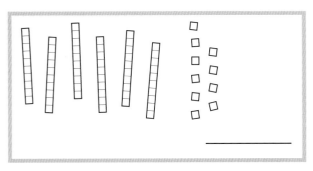
_____

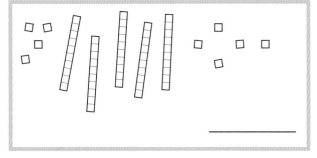
_____

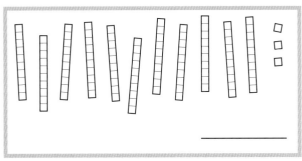
_____

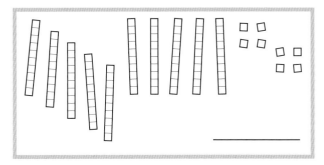
_____

Number Connections © Rose Griffiths 200
Harcourt Education Lt

Number words

Name _____

Date _____

Use a pencil. Write in CAPITAL letters.

Clues

Across:

3 Four add four

5 Eighteen take away seven

6 Eight take away five

Down:

1 Four add three

2 Thirty take away ten

4 Eighty add twenty

Clues

Across:

3 Two add two

5 Nine add nine

7 Two add eighteen

8 One take away one

Down:

1 Six, nine and twelve are all m _ _ _ _ _ _ _ _ of three

2 Seven days

4 Special word for a hundred

6 Four is not odd, it is _ _ _ _

7 Five add five

Spelling number words
◄ Green Pupil Book Part 3 pages 70 and 71
► Copymaster G64

Number Connections © Rose Griffiths 2005
Harcourt Education Ltd

Number words

Name _____

Date _____

Use a pencil. Write in CAPITAL letters.

Clues

Across:

1 Two add one

5 Two weeks

6 One add one

8 Forty add fifty

Down:

2 Fifty add fifty

3 Forty add forty

4 Special word for twelve

7 Five is not even it is _ _ _

Clues

Across:

2 Two add three

6 [calculator]

7 Five take away four

8 Thirty add thirty

Down:

1 On a calculator, the answer is on the D _ _ _ _ _ _

3 Eight add eight

4 There are sixty _ _ _ _ _ _ _ in a minute

5 Twenty add twenty

Four times table

Name _____

Date _____

Cut out the eleven tables facts.
Fold along the dotted line and glue flat.

Ask your teacher how to practise with these.

		5×4	20
0×4	0	6×4	24
1×4	4	7×4	28
2×4	8	8×4	32
3×4	12	9×4	36
4×4	16	10×4	40

Number Connections © Rose Griffiths 2005
Harcourt Education Ltd

Four times table

Name _____

Date _____

Fill in the missing numbers.

Check.

$4 \times 10 =$ ☐
$10 \times 4 =$ ☐

$5 \times 4 =$ ☐
$4 \times 5 =$ ☐

$6 \times 4 =$ ☐
$4 \times 6 =$ ☐

$8 \times 4 =$ ☐
$4 \times 8 =$ ☐

$10 \times 4 =$ ☐
☐ $\times 4 = 36$
$8 \times 4 =$ ☐
$7 \times 4 =$ ☐
☐ $\times 4 = 24$
$5 \times 4 =$ ☐
$4 \times 4 =$ ☐
☐ $\times 4 = 12$
$2 \times 4 =$ ☐
$1 \times 4 =$ ☐
$0 \times 4 =$ ☐

What is
7 times 4?

_____

What is
4 times 7?

_____

Games

Name _____

Date _____

Fill in the missing numbers.

5 + ☐ = 15	☐ + 1 = 15
7 + ☐ = 15	☐ + 3 = 15
2 + ☐ = 15	☐ + 8 = 15
6 + ☐ = 15	☐ + 14 = 15
0 + ☐ = 15	☐ + 11 = 15
10 + ☐ = 15	☐ + 7 = 15
13 + ☐ = 15	☐ + 9 = 15
4 + ☐ = 15	☐ + 10 = 15
15 + ☐ = 15	☐ + 12 = 15

7 + ☐ = 15
☐ + 7 = 15

9 + ☐ = 15
☐ + 9 = 15

10 + ☐ = 15
☐ + 10 = 15

8 + ☐ = 15
☐ + 8 = 15

Games

Name _____

Date _____

Do these as quickly as you can.

15 − 5 = ___	15 − 1 = ___	15 − 3 = ___
15 − 8 = ___	15 − 9 = ___	15 − 7 = ___
15 − 2 = ___	15 − 6 = ___	15 −12 = ___
15 − 0 = ___	15 −11 = ___	15 − 4 = ___
15 −14 = ___	15 −13 = ___	15 −10 = ___

 ✓ or ✗

How much money left?

_____

How much money left?

_____

How much money left?

_____

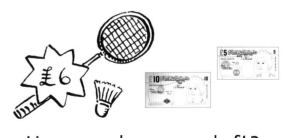

How much money left?

_____

Addition and subtraction bonds to 15 ◀ Green Pupil Book Part 3 pages 74 and 75

Number Connections © Rose Griffiths 200
Harcourt Education Lt

What comes next?

Name _____

Date _____

Fill in the missing numbers.

Add 3.

| 3 | 6 | 9 | 12 | | | | |

| 2 | 5 | 8 | 11 | | | | |

| 1 | 4 | 7 | 10 | | | | |

Add 2.

| 3 | 5 | 7 | 9 | | | | |

| 2 | 4 | | | | | | |

| 1 | 3 | | | | | | |

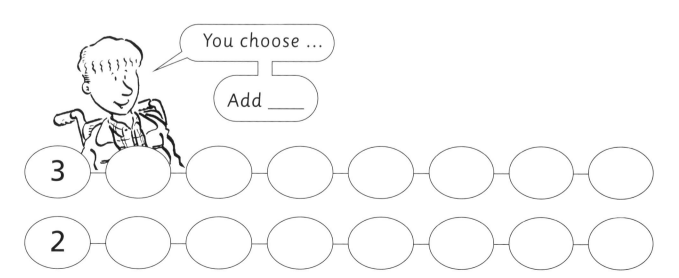

You choose ...

Add ____

| 3 | | | | | | | |

| 2 | | | | | | | |

What comes next?

Name _____

Date _____

Join the dots in order. Start at 0.

- 21
- 18
- 24
- 15
- 33
- 36
- 39
- 42
- 27
- 30
- 9
- 45
- 12
- 48
- 6
- 51
- 3
- 54
- 0
- 60
- 57

Number Connections © Rose Griffiths 20C
Harcourt Education Lt

Speedy sums Ⓜ

1 2 3 minute test

Name _____

Date _____

7 + 6 + 2 = _____   6 + 8 = _____   15 – 7 = _____

4 + 7 + 4 = _____   3 +11 = _____   12 – 7 = _____

2 + 1 +12 = _____   7 + 8 = _____   6 – 6 = _____

2 + 2 + 9 = _____   6 + 6 = _____   13 – 4 = _____

6 + 3 + 4 = _____   5 + 8 = _____   14 – 8 = _____

5 + 7 + 3 = _____   9 + 6 = _____   10 – 6 = _____

0 + 7 + 7 = _____   4 +11 = _____   Score: _____

Mental recall of bonds within 15 ◄ Green Pupil Book Part 3
pages 78 and 79 onwards

Number Connections © Rose Griffiths 2005
Harcourt Education Ltd

Speedy sums Ⓝ

1 2 3 minute test

Name _____

Date _____

3 + 7 + 2 = _____   2 +13 = _____   14 – 9 = _____

5 + 3 + 5 = _____   0 +11 = _____   15 – 8 = _____

4 + 3 + 6 = _____   8 + 7 = _____   8 – 7 = _____

7 + 1 + 3 = _____   6 + 9 = _____   11 – 6 = _____

6 + 4 + 5 = _____   4 +11 = _____   13 – 5 = _____

2 + 3 + 9 = _____   7 + 7 = _____   10 – 7 = _____

5 + 5 + 5 = _____   8 + 6 = _____   Score: _____

Mental recall of bonds within 15 ◄ Green Pupil Book Part 3
pages 78 and 79 onwards

Number Connections © Rose Griffiths 2005
Harcourt Education Ltd

Number line

Name _____

Date _____

Cut along here very carefully.

Make your own number line.

- Write your name, and the missing numbers.
- Cut out the 3 strips.
- Glue them together in the right order.

This number line belongs to _____

0 1 2 3 4 5 6 7 8 9 10 11 12 13 14 15 19 2

GLUE

0 21 22 25 30 31 34 35 39 4

GLUE

0 41 44 45 48 50 55 57 58 60

Addition and subtraction within 60
◄ Green Pupil Book Part 3 pages 80 and 81
► Copymasters G73 and G74

Number Connections © Rose Griffiths 2005
Harcourt Education Ltd

Number line

Name _____

Date _____

Use tens and ones
on your number line.

---

24 + 31 = _____

20 + 4 + 30 + 1 = _____

20 + 30 + 4 + 1 = _____

4 + 1 + 20 + 30 = _____

---

39 + 18 = _____

30 + 9 + 10 + 8 = _____

30 + 10 + 9 + 8 = _____

9 + 8 + 30 + 10 = _____

---

17 + 26 = _____

10 + 7 + 20 + 6 = _____

10 + 20 + 7 + 6 = _____

7 + 6 + 10 + 20 = _____

---

15 + 32 = _____

10 + 5 + 30 + 2 = _____

10 + 30 + 5 + 2 = _____

5 + 2 + 10 + 30 = _____

---

41 + 14 = _____

40 + 1 + 10 + 4 = _____

40 + 10 + 1 + 4 = _____

1 + 4 + 40 + 10 = _____

---

34 + 25 = _____

30 + 4 + 20 + 5 = _____

30 + 20 + 4 + 5 = _____

4 + 5 + 30 + 20 = _____

---

33 + 27 = _____

30 + 3 + 20 + 7 = _____

30 + 20 + 3 + 7 = _____

3 + 7 + 30 + 20 = _____

---

19 + 29 = _____

10 + 9 + 20 + 9 = _____

10 + 20 + 9 + 9 = _____

9 + 9 + 10 + 20 = _____

Addition and subtraction within 60   ◀ Green Pupil Book Part 3 pages 80 and 81
▶ Copymaster G74

Number line

Name _____

Date _____

Write each sum and work it out.

Check on your number line.

Twenty-five add eleven.

$$\begin{array}{r} 25 \\ + 11 \\ \hline \\ \hline \end{array}$$

Thirty-five add eight.

Forty-eight take away twenty-five.

Twenty-seven take away four.

Twenty-nine add twenty-eight.

Fifty-eight take away twenty-eight.

Seven add forty-four.

Fifty-two take away thirty-three.

Four cards

Name _____

Date _____

 $4 \times 1 =$ _____

 $4 \times 2 =$ _____

 $4 \times 3 =$ _____

 $4 \times 4 =$ _____

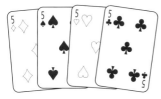 $4 \times 5 =$ _____

 $4 \times 6 =$ _____

 $4 \times 7 =$ _____

 $4 \times 8 =$ _____

 $4 \times 9 =$ _____

 $4 \times 10 =$ _____

$3 \times 4 =$ _____ $7 \times 4 =$ _____ $1 \times 4 =$ _____

$5 \times 4 =$ _____ $2 \times 4 =$ _____ $6 \times 4 =$ _____

$9 \times 4 =$ _____ $8 \times 4 =$ _____ $4 \times 4 =$ _____

$0 \times 4 =$ _____ $10 \times 4 =$ _____

Mixed problems   ◀ Green Pupil Book Part 3 pages 82 and 83
                     ▶ Copymaster G76

Number Connections © Rose Griffiths 2005
Harcourt Education Ltd

Four cards

Name _____

Date _____

Write the missing numbers.

These add up to 23 ...

so this must be 7.

These add up to 21.

These add up to 22.

These add up to 18.

These add up to 31.

These add up to 14.

These add up to 17.

These add up to 27.

 ✓ or ✗

Twins

Name _____

Date _____

Half each.

Half of 8 is _____

Half of 9 is _____

Use strawberries! (or counters) then a calculator.

Half of 18 is _____ | 1 | 8 | ÷ | 2 | = | _____

Half of 22 is _____ | 2 | 2 | ÷ | 2 | = | _____

Half of 25 is _____ | 2 | 5 | ÷ | 2 | = | _____

Half of 37 is _____ | 3 | 7 | ÷ | 2 | = | _____

Half of 38 is _____ | 3 | 8 | ÷ | 2 | = | _____

Half of 44 is _____ | 4 | 4 | ÷ | 2 | = | _____

Half of 52 is _____ | 5 | 2 | ÷ | 2 | = | _____

Half of 56 is _____ | 5 | 6 | ÷ | 2 | = | _____

Half of 57 is _____ | 5 | 7 | ÷ | 2 | = | _____

Halving and doubling   ◄ Green Pupil Book Part 3 pages 84 and 85
                            ► Copymaster G78

Twins

Name _____

Date _____

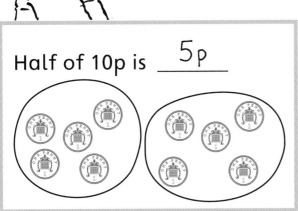

We're sharing money.

Sometimes there is one penny left over.

remainder

Half of 10p is ___5p___

Half of 11p is ___5p r.1p___

Use pennies or counters, then a calculator.

Half of 20p is _____   20 ÷ 2 = _____

Half of 34p is _____   34 ÷ 2 = _____

Half of 44p is _____   44 ÷ 2 = _____

Half of 45p is _____   45 ÷ 2 = _____

Half of 29p is _____   29 ÷ 2 = _____

Half of 33p is _____   33 ÷ 2 = _____

Half of 48p is _____   48 ÷ 2 = _____

Half of 53p is _____   53 ÷ 2 = _____

Half of 59p is _____   59 ÷ 2 = _____

Number Connections © Rose Griffiths 2005
Harcourt Education Ltd

Quarter hours

Name _____

Date _____

Use a real clock.

Make the clock show each time.
Then draw it.

One o'clock	Quarter past one	Half past one
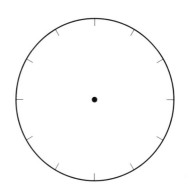	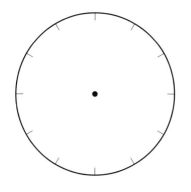	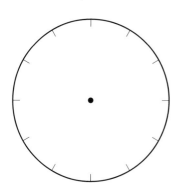
Quarter to two	Two o'clock	Quarter past two
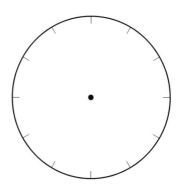	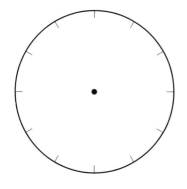	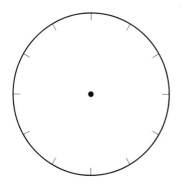
Half past two	Quarter to three	Three o'clock
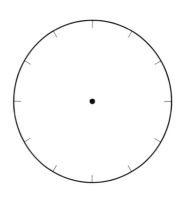	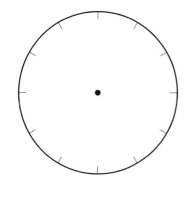	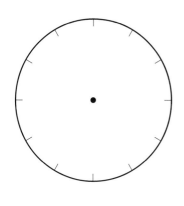

Quarter hours

Name _____

Date _____

What's the time?

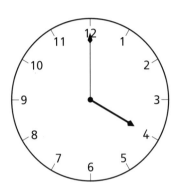

4 o'clock

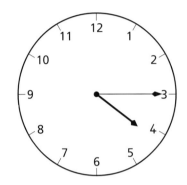

Quarter past _____

Half past _____

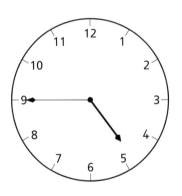

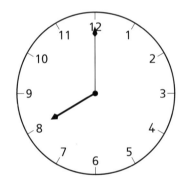

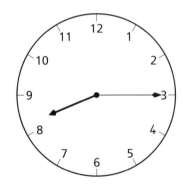

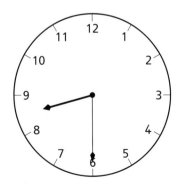

Making sixty

Name _____

Date _____

Use tens and ones
on your number line.

Fill in the missing numbers.

47 + ☐ = 60   16 + ☐ = 60

☐ + 28 = 60   9 + ☐ = 60

31 + ☐ = 60   ☐ + 52 = 60

46 + ☐ = 60   24 + ☐ = 60

Use tens and ones.
Then take away on paper.

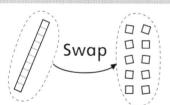

Swap

```
   60        60        60        60
 - 13      - 32      - 29      - 14
 _____     _____     _____     _____

 _____     _____     _____     _____


   60        60        60        60
 - 44      - 51      -  8      - 36
 _____     _____     _____     _____

 _____     _____     _____     _____
```

Making sixty

Name _____

Date _____

Fill in the missing numbers.

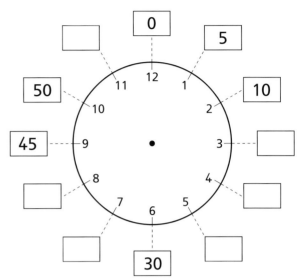

[ ] minutes in an hour

[ ] minutes in quarter of an hour

[ ] minutes in half an hour

Use a real clock with hands.

Make the clock show each time. Then draw it.

Quarter past seven

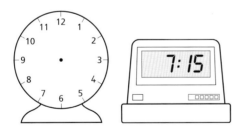

7:15

Twenty-five past seven

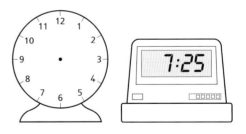

7:25

Quarter to eight

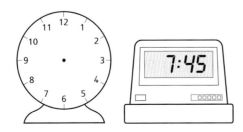

7:45

Ten to eight

7:50

Pens in packs

Name _____

Date _____

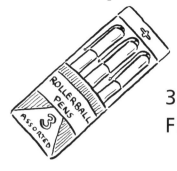

3 pens in a pack.
Fill in the missing numbers.

Number of packs	How many pens?
0	
1	3
2	
3	
4	
5	
6	
7	
8	
9	
10	

$0 \times 3 =$ _____

$1 \times 3 =$ _____

$2 \times 3 =$ _____

$3 \times 3 =$ _____

$4 \times 3 =$ _____

$5 \times 3 =$ _____

$6 \times 3 =$ _____

$7 \times 3 =$ _____

$8 \times 3 =$ _____

$9 \times 3 =$ _____

$10 \times 3 =$ _____

☐ $\div 3 = 0$

☐ $\div 3 = 1$

☐ $\div 3 = 2$

☐ $\div 3 = 3$

☐ $\div 3 = 4$

☐ $\div 3 = 5$

☐ $\div 3 = 6$

☐ $\div 3 = 7$

☐ $\div 3 = 8$

☐ $\div 3 = 9$

☐ $\div 3 = 10$

7 packs.
How many pens?

_____

24 pens.
How many packs?

_____

Pens in packs

Name _____

Date _____

5 pens in a pack.
Fill in the missing numbers.

Number of packs	How many pens?
0	
1	5
2	
3	
4	

Number of packs	How many pens?
5	
6	
7	
8	
9	
10	

9 packs.
How many pens?

25 pens.
How many packs?

_____   _____

5 × 4 = _____   30 ÷ 5 = _____   2 × 5 = _____

5 × 7 = _____   50 ÷ 5 = _____   5 × 5 = _____

5 × 3 = _____   35 ÷ 5 = _____   9 × 5 = _____

5 × 8 = _____   20 ÷ 5 = _____   0 × 5 = _____

5 × 6 = _____   45 ÷ 5 = _____   7 × 5 = _____

Day trip

Name _____

Date _____

Make up your own list of coach trips.

Fill in the spaces.

_____'s Coaches

Trips run every

Ticket prices

Adult: £ _____

Child: £ _____

Trips run every

Ticket prices

Adult: £ _____

Child: £ _____

Trips run every

Ticket prices

Adult: £ _____

Child: £ _____

Cut out. Use with Copymaster G86. Ask your teacher how to play.

- Your name
- Names of places to visit
- Pictures
- Days
- Price of tickets

Mixed problems

◀ Green Pupil Book Part 3 pages 92 and 93

▶ Copymaster G86

Number Connections © Rose Griffiths 2005

Harcourt Education Ltd

Day trip

Name _____

Date _____

Use with Copymaster G85. Ask your teacher how to play.

✂   ✂   ✂

_____'s Coaches	_____'s Coaches
Trip to _____	Trip to _____
Date _____ £ _____	Date _____ £ _____

_____'s Coaches	_____'s Coaches
Trip to _____	Trip to _____
Date _____ £ _____	Date _____ £ _____

_____'s Coaches	_____'s Coaches
Trip to _____	Trip to _____
Date _____ £ _____	Date _____ £ _____

_____'s Coaches	_____'s Coaches
Trip to _____	Trip to _____
Date _____ £ _____	Date _____ £ _____

_____'s Coaches	_____'s Coaches
Trip to _____	Trip to _____
Date _____ £ _____	Date _____ £ _____

In your head

Name _____

Date _____

Do these in your head.

45 + 10 = _____   25 + 30 = _____

59 − 20 = _____   34 + 20 = _____

19 + 30 = _____   18 + 40 = _____

32 + 20 = _____   57 − 40 = _____

58 − 30 = _____   46 + 10 = _____

27 + 20 = _____   30 + 30 = _____

52 − 20 = _____   29 + 30 = _____

✓ or ✗

```
   43        54        60        37
 − 30      − 30      − 40      − 30
 ____      ____      ____      ____

 ____      ____      ____      ____
```

```
   28        40        23        20
 + 30      + 15      + 30      + 36
 ____      ____      ____      ____

 ____      ____      ____      ____
```

In your head

Work with a friend.
Talk about these sums.

Cut them out.
Sort them into 2 piles.
Stick them in your book in 2 groups.

Sums I can do in my head.		Sums I need to write down.	
Fifty-one take away twenty-six	Twenty-five add twenty-eight	Forty add twenty	Sixty take away forty-eight
Twenty-two add thirty-three	Sixty take away thirty-three	Fifty-six take away thirty-nine	Forty-two add fifteen

Print on card if possible. Reusable.
Cut out the instructions card and 20 number cards.
Store in a clear zip-top wallet or in an envelope.

≈ Fifteens ≈

A game for 1, 2 or 3 people.

- **Before you start**
  Shuffle the number cards.
  Spread them out on the table, face down.

- **How to play**

Turn over 2 cards.
Add up the numbers.

If you get exactly 15,
<u>keep</u> the cards.
If not, turn the cards
back over.

Now it is your
friend's go.

- **Keep going until all the cards have gone.**

◀ Green Pupil Book Part 3; **Addition and subtraction bonds to 15**

Number Connections © Rose Griffiths 2005
Harcourt Education Ltd

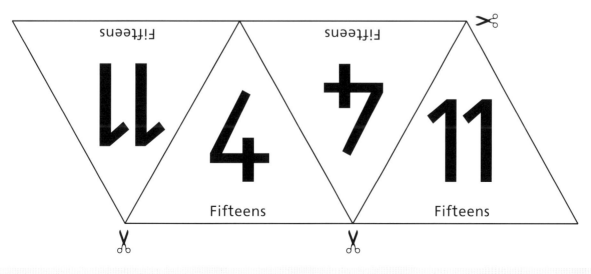

Print on card if possible. Reusable.

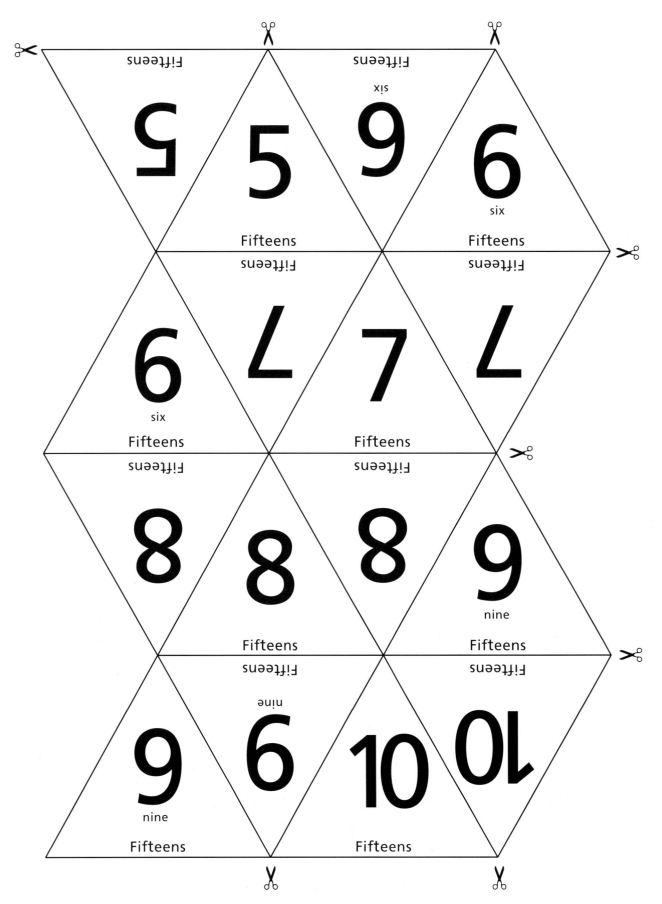

Double your money

Print on card if possible. Reusable.
Colour in and cover with clear plastic if wished, then cut out the two pieces of the board.
Use sticky tape to fasten them together.

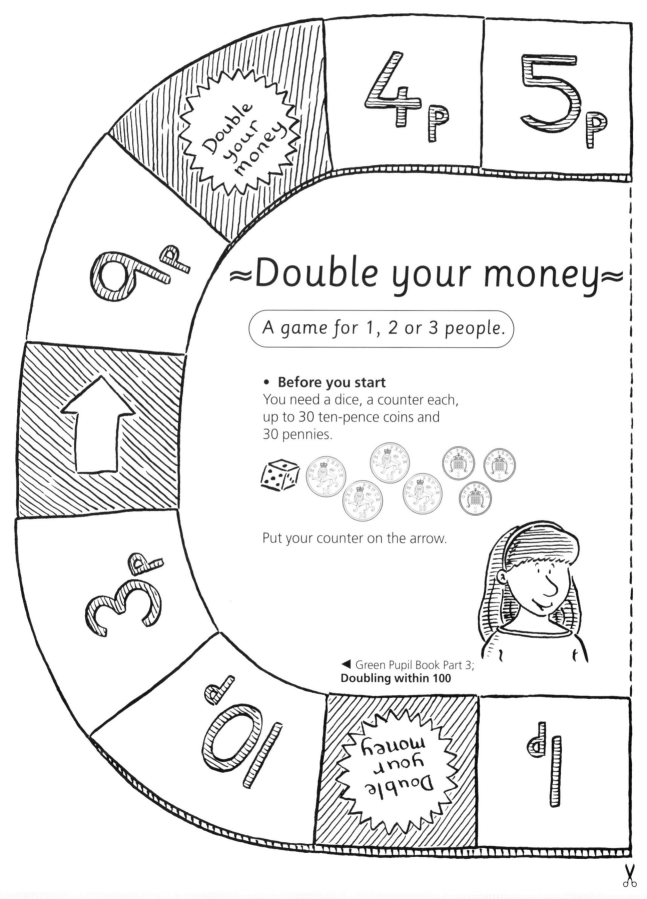

4p

5p

Double your money

9p

≈Double your money≈

A game for 1, 2 or 3 people.

3p

• **Before you start**
You need a dice, a counter each,
up to 30 ten-pence coins and
30 pennies.

Put your counter on the arrow.

10p

Double your money

1p

◄ Green Pupil Book Part 3;
Doubling within 100

Double your money

sheet 2 of 2

Print on card if possible. Reusable.
Store in a clear zip-top wallet or in an envelope.
If possible, include a dice, 3 counters, 30 plastic or card ten-pence coins and 30 pennies.

Throw the dice and move that number of spaces.

Take the amount of money you land on. <u>Double</u> your money if you land there!

How much money have you got now?

Now it is your friend's go.

The winner is the first person to have more than £1.

Number Connections © Rose Griffiths 2005
Harcourt Education Ltd